# GEORG FRIEDRICH H[ÄNDEL]

# »DETTINGER« TE DEUM

für drei Solostimmen, Chor und Orchester

# TE DEUM FOR THE VICTORY OF DETTINGEN

for three Soloists, Chorus and Orchestra

## HWV 283

Ausgabe nach den Quellen von / Edition based on original sources by

## Carl Eberhardt

Klavierauszug / Vocal Score

EIGENTUM DES VERLEGERS · ALLE RECHTE VORBEHALTEN
ALL RIGHTS RESERVED

# C. F. PETERS

FRANKFURT/M. · LEIPZIG · LONDON · NEW YORK

# INHALT/CONTENTS

# Vorwort

Für die Feierlichkeiten des Sieges der alliierten Engländer und Österreicher über die Franzosen am 27. Juni 1743 in Dettingen am Main komponierte Händel, seit 1723 Hofkomponist, im Juli/August 1743 das vorliegende Te Deum nebst dem *Anthem for the Victory of Dettingen (The King shall rejoice;* HWV 265). Nach seinem *Utrechter Te Deum* von 1713 (HWV 278), das Purcells Te Deum von 1694 aus den festlichen Gottesdiensten verdrängt hatte, löste das *Dettinger Te Deum* seinerseits die Komposition zum Utrechter Frieden ab. Die (offizielle) Aufführung des *Dettinger Te Deum* in Anwesenheit von König Georg II. fand am 27. November 1743 in der Chapel Royal von St. James statt; drei, vielleicht auch vier öffentliche Proben waren ihr vorausgegangen.

Nachdem das Benefizkonzert vom 28. März 1738 Händel nur knapp vor dem finanziellen Desaster seiner letzten Opernunternehmung rettete (am 10. Februar 1741 war das Unternehmen endgültig zu Ende), wandte er sich verstärkt den verschiedenen oratorischen Gattungen zu. *L'Allegro, il Penseroso ed il Moderato,* sowie *Saul,* der *Messias* und *Joseph and his brethren,* dem Händel den Schlußsatz des *Anthem for the Victory of Dettingen* einverleibte, mögen hier als Markierungspunkte der Entstehungszeit des *Dettinger Te Deum* genügen. Über die zeitgenössische Aufnahme dieses Te Deum gibt ein Auszug aus dem »Daily Advertiser« Auskunft: »Gestern wurde vor einer glänzenden Versammlung in der Whitehall Chapel ein 'Te Deum' und ein Anthem geprobt, die Herr Händel im Auftrag Seiner Majestät komponierte. Diese Werke werden von den maßgeblichen Musikkennern für derart meisterhaft und erhaben sowie in ihrer Art neu gehalten, daß sie dieses Genie nicht nur als unerschöpflich erweisen, sondern auch Zeugnis dafür ablegen, daß sein Genie zu einem noch höheren Grade der Vollständigkeit immer weiter emporsteigt.«[1]

Wie in seinen anderen Te Deum-Kompositionen vertonte Händel auch hier den Ambrosianischen Lobgesang in englischer Übersetzung. Der lateinische Hymnus findet sich im Stundengebet (Matutin) der römisch-katholischen Liturgie und ist in der Übersetzung Bestandteil des Morning-Service der anglikanischen Kirche. Spätestens seit der zweiten Hälfte des 16. Jahrhunderts wurde das Te Deum darüberhinaus auch bei offiziellen Festgottesdiensten gesungen. So ist auch das *Dettinger Te Deum,* ebenso wie das *Utrechter Te Deum* und die *Coronation Anthems,* dem repräsentativen, zeremoniellen Glanz verpflichtet; gerade die genannten Werke galten der unmittelbar nach Händels Tod einsetzenden englischen Musikgeschichtsschreibung — etwa Hawkins — exemplarisch für Händels Genie: »Kein Kenner der Vorteile der Händelschen Musik würde je zögern, sein erstes 'Te Deum', das 'Jubilate', seine Krönungs- und andere Hymnen, das sogenannte 'Dettinger Te Deum' sowie die Chorsätze seiner Oratorien in die erste und oberste Kategorie seines Schaffens einzustufen.«[2]

Im Werk selbst geht Händel, in der äußeren Anlage etwa, auf eigene wie auf fremde Kompositionen (Purcell) zurück. Vor allem das um 1700 entstandene Te Deum des italienischen Franziskaners Francesco Antonio Urio hat, weniger in der formalen Disposition als in der thematischen Erfindung, deutlichen Einfluß auf Händel gehabt. Über die Bezüge im Detail gibt der zweite Band des Händel-Handbuchs erschöpfend Auskunft[3]. Der emphatische Jubel der großzügigen Chorsätze (»Wir preisen dich, Gott« und »Vor dir Cherubim und Seraphim«), den Händel wie kein zweiter in eine zeitlose, eindringliche Klangpracht zu verwandeln wußte, wird durch die gegenübergestellten, verinnerlichten Abschnitte (»Als du auf dich genommen«) nur bewußt verstärkt. Die barocke Geisteshaltung kommt aber nicht nur in der zeittypischen Kontrastierung zum Vorschein, sondern auch in den affektiven, bildhaft-rhetorischen Figuren: So in den durchlaufenden, scheinbar endlosen Punktierungen »... von Ewigkeit zu Ewigkeit singen sie vor dir...« oder im schmerzlich-dissonierenden »Als du siegreich zerbrachst den Stachel des Todes«.

Gegenüber der „romantisch" überzeichneten Dynamik und Artikulation früherer Ausgaben wurde der vorliegende Klavierauszug nach neuen musikwissenschaftlichen Erkenntnissen gestaltet: Die in Klammern gesetzten Vortragsbezeichnungen verstehen sich als aufführungspraktische Hinweise. Denn Händels Chöre verdienen es, wie schon Sulzer 1771 in seiner *Allgemeinen Theorie der Schönen Künste* feststellte, »... mit der grössten Überlegung studirt zu werden.«[4]

*Peter Lüttig*

---

[1] Daily Advertiser vom 19. November 1743; In: Handel, A documentary Biography by O. E. Deutsch. London, 1955

[2] J. Hawkins. A General History of the science and practice of Music. London, 1776

[3] Händel-Handbuch Bd. II: Thematisch-systematisches Verzeichnis: Oratorische Werke, Vokale Kammermusik, Kirchenmusik. Von Bernd Baselt. Kassel, 1984

[4] J. G. Sulzer. Allgemeine Theorie der Schönen Künste. Leipzig, 1771 und öfter.

# Preface

In July and August of 1743 Händel, who was court composer in England from 1723, wrote this present setting of the *Te Deum*, together with an *Anthem for the Victory of Dettingen* (*The King shall rejoice*, HWV 265), for the festivities celebrating the victory of the allied English and Austrians over the French at Dettingen am Main on 27 July 1743, Previously, his *Utrecht Te Deum* of 1713 (HWV 278) had supplanted Purcell's *Te Deum* setting of 1694 in festive church services; now the *Dettingen Te Deum* did the same to his own setting for the Peace of Utrecht. The official performance of the *Dettingen Te Deum*, preceded by three and perhaps four public rehearsals, took place on 27 November 1743 in the Chapel Royal of St James in the presence of King George II.

On 28 March 1738, in the nick of time, Handel was rescued by a benefit concert from the financial disaster of his final opera venture (it collapsed on 10 February 1741). Thereafter he turned increasingly to various species of oratorio. His *L'Allegro, il Penseroso ed il Moderato*, *Saul*, *The Messiah* and *Joseph and his Brethren* (incorporating the final movement of his *Anthem for the Victory of Dettingen*) suffice to show the milestones on his path to the *Dettingen Te Deum*. An excerpt from the *Daily Advertiser* sheds light on the contemporary reception of this work:

»Yesterday a *Te Deum* and Anthem, composed by Mr. Handel for his Majesty, were rehearsed before a splendid Assembly at Whitehall Chapel, and are said by the best Judges to be so truly masterly and sublime, as well as new in their kind, that they prove this Genius not only exhaustible, but likewise still rising to a higher Degree of Perfection.«[1]

As in his other *Te Deum* settings, Handel set an English translation of St. Ambrose's hymn of praise. The Latin version is found in the canonical hours of the Roman Catholic liturgy, namely in the Matins. Translated into English, it then was made part of the morning service of the Anglican Church. The *Te Deum* was also sung at official church services at least from the midsixteenth century. Accordingly, like the *Utrecht Te Deum* and his *Coronation Anthems*, Handel's *Dettingen Te Deum* is a work designed for ceremonial pomp. Indeed, these very works were considered prime examples of Handel's genius by the English school of music historians that emerged in the years immediately following his death. Hawkins, for example, writes:

»In the first and highest class of Handel's works no competent judge of their merits would hesitate to rank his first *Te Deum*, and the *Jubilate*, his coronation and other anthems, the *Dettingen Te Deum*, as it is called, and the chorusses in his oratories.«[2]

Handel took earlier works by himself and others (e. g. Purcell) as models for his setting, for example in its large-scale design. In particular, he was clearly influenced by a *Te Deum* written around 1700 by Francesco Antonio Urio, an Italian of the Franciscan order, though less by its formal layout than by its themes. The relation between these works is exhaustively discussed in volume 2 of the *Händel-Handbuch*.[3] The triumphant jubilation of the grand choral movements (»We praise Thee, oh God« and »To Thee Cherubim and Seraphim«), which Handel was able to transform like no composer before or since into a timeless and urgent panoply of sound, is deliberately magnified all the more by the meditative sections (»When Thou tookest upon Thee«). Handel's Baroque cast of mind comes to the fore not only in these contrasts, which were typical of their time, but also in his use of rhetorical »figures«, emotion-laden pictorial symbols such as the seemingly endless dotted figures at »... continually, continually do cry...« or the heartfelt dissonance at »When Thou hadst overcome the sharpness of death.««

Unlike the excessively "romanticized" dynamics and articulation of earlier editions, this piano-vocal score has made use of recent musicological discoveries. Expression marks enclosed in brackets indicate suggestions for performance practice. In the end, as Sulzer remarked in 1771 in his *Allgemeine Theorie der Schönen Künste*, Handel's choruses deserve »to be studied with utmost care and deliberation.«[4]

*Peter Lüttig*

---

[1]  *Daily Advertiser* (19 November 1743); cited in O. E. Deutsch: *Handel: a Documentary Biography*
    (London, 1955).
[2]  J. Hawkins: *A General History of the Science and Practice of Music* (London, 1776).
[3]  Bernd Baselt: *Thematisch-systematisches Verzeichnis: Oratorische Werke, Vokale Kammermusik,
    Kirchenmusik*. Händel-Handbuch, ii (Kassel, 1984).
[4]  J. G. Sulzer: *Allgemeine Theorie der Schönen Künste* (Leipzig, 1771) with many reissues.

```
┌─────────────────────────────────────────────┐
│                                               │
│         INSTRUMENTE DES ORCHESTERS            │
│                                               │
│       2 Oboen – Fagott – 2 Trompeten          │
│            Prinzipal – Pauken                 │
│      Violine I – Violine II – Violine III     │
│      Viola – Violoncello – Kontrabaß          │
│            Orgel – Cembalo                     │
│                                               │
└─────────────────────────────────────────────┘
```

Aufführungsdauer / *Duration: ca. 50 Min.*

Aufführungsmaterial käuflich und leihweise
*Orchestra material is available on sale or rental*

# »Dettinger« Te Deum
## Te Deum for the victory of Dettingen

### Nr. 1 Chor

Georg Friedrich Händel (1685-1759)
HWV 283

4

6

7

8

12

13

14

## Nr. 2 Solo und Chor

18

+ Ob. Fag. Str. Org.

20

Edition Peters                    31568

22

24

# Nr. 3 Chor

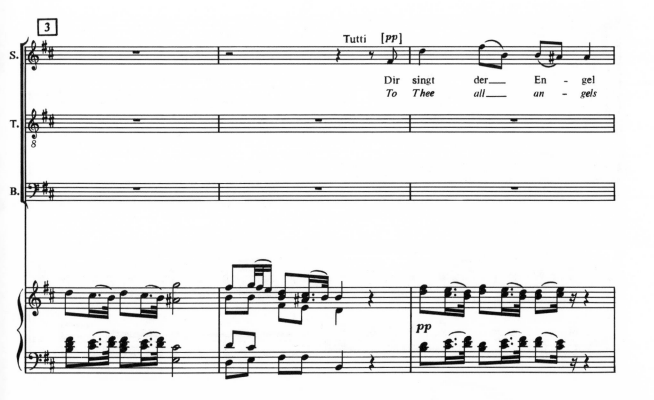

26

# Nr. 4 Chor

31568

32

36

38

# Nr. 5 Chor

44

46

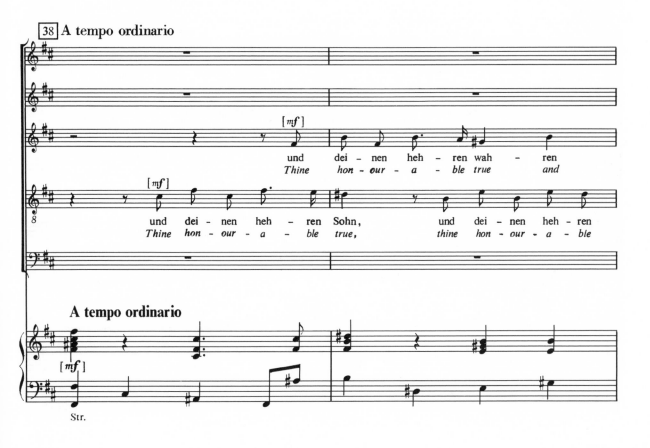

48

## Nr. 6 Solo und Chor

Tr. Ob.

du bist in E - wig - keit      der     Sohn   des All - va - - ters.
*Thou art the e - ver - last - ing     Son   of   the Fa - - ther.*

Tutti

# Nr. 7 Arie

**Larghetto, e piano un poco**

[p]

**8**

**15** Basso solo [p]

B.

Als du auf dich ge - nommen die Er - lö-sung der Welt,
*When Thou took-est up - on Thee to de - li - ver man,*

Str. *tr* Str.

Cemb. Cemb.

**22**

B.

hast du nicht ver - schmäht, _____
*Thou didst not ab - hor, _____*

Cemb.

31568

57

A

hast du nicht ver-schmäht ___ der ___ Mensch-heit Los;
*Thou didst not ab - hor ___ the Vir - gin's womb;*

Str.

als du auf dich ge - nom-men ___ als du auf dich ge-
*when Thou took-est up - on Thee, ___ when Thou took-est up -*

Cemb.　　　　　　　Cemb.

nom - men ___ die Er - lö-sung der Welt,
*on Thee ___ to de - li - ver man,*

Viol.　　　　Viol.

Cemb.

hast ___ du nicht ver-schmäht ___
*Thou ___ didst not ab - hor ___*

Cemb.

58

# Nr. 8 Chor

61

62

31568

64

65

66

# Nr. 9 Trio

68

70

Nr. 10 [Sinfonia]

# Nr. 11 Chor

31568

## Nr. 12 Chor

31568

74

# Nr. 13 Chor

78

83

84

## Nr. 14 Accompagnato

88

# Nr. 15 Solo und Chor

93

94

98

Edition Peters

31568

## MUSIK FÜR GEMISCHTEN CHOR
### (weltlich)
#### a cappella oder mit Klavier

### C. F. PETERS · FRANKFURT/M. · LEIPZIG · LONDON · NEW YORK
www.edition-peters.de · www.edition-peters.com